Color Key

1. black
2. gray
3. brown
4. beige
5. pink
6. red
7. light yellow
8. green
9. dark green
10. blue-green

Squirrel & Chipmunk

Color Key

① black
② gray
③ brown
④ beige
⑤ pink
⑥ yellow
⑦ light yellow
⑧ light green
⑨ dark green
⑩ blue-green

Bear & Deer

Color Key

1. black
2. gray
3. brown
4. pink
5. yellow
6. light yellow
7. green
8. dark green
9. light blue
10. white

Bald Eagle

Color Key
1 black
2 brown
3 beige
4 pink
5 red
6 yellow
7 light yellow
8 light green
9 green
10 blue

Prairie Dog

Mountain Goat

Color Key
1. gray
2. brown
3. beige
4. pink
5. red
6. orange
7. yellow
8. green
9. dark green
10. blue-green

Shrew

Color Key

1 black
2 gray
3 brown
4 magenta
5 pink
6 red
7 orange
8 green
9 blue
10 white

Moose

Color Key

1. gray
2. brown
3. beige
4. pink
5. light yellow
6. green
7. dark green
8. blue
9. light blue
10. white

Beaver

Color Key
1 black
2 gray
3 brown
4 beige
5 red
6 yellow
7 light green
8 green
9 dark green
10 light blue

Coyote

Loon

Color Key

1 black
2 gray
3 brown
4 beige
5 magenta
6 pink
7 red
8 light green
9 blue-green
10 white

Aardvark

Color Key

1 black
2 gray
3 brown
4 beige
5 magenta
6 pink
7 red
8 light green
9 dark green
10 light blue

Hedgehog

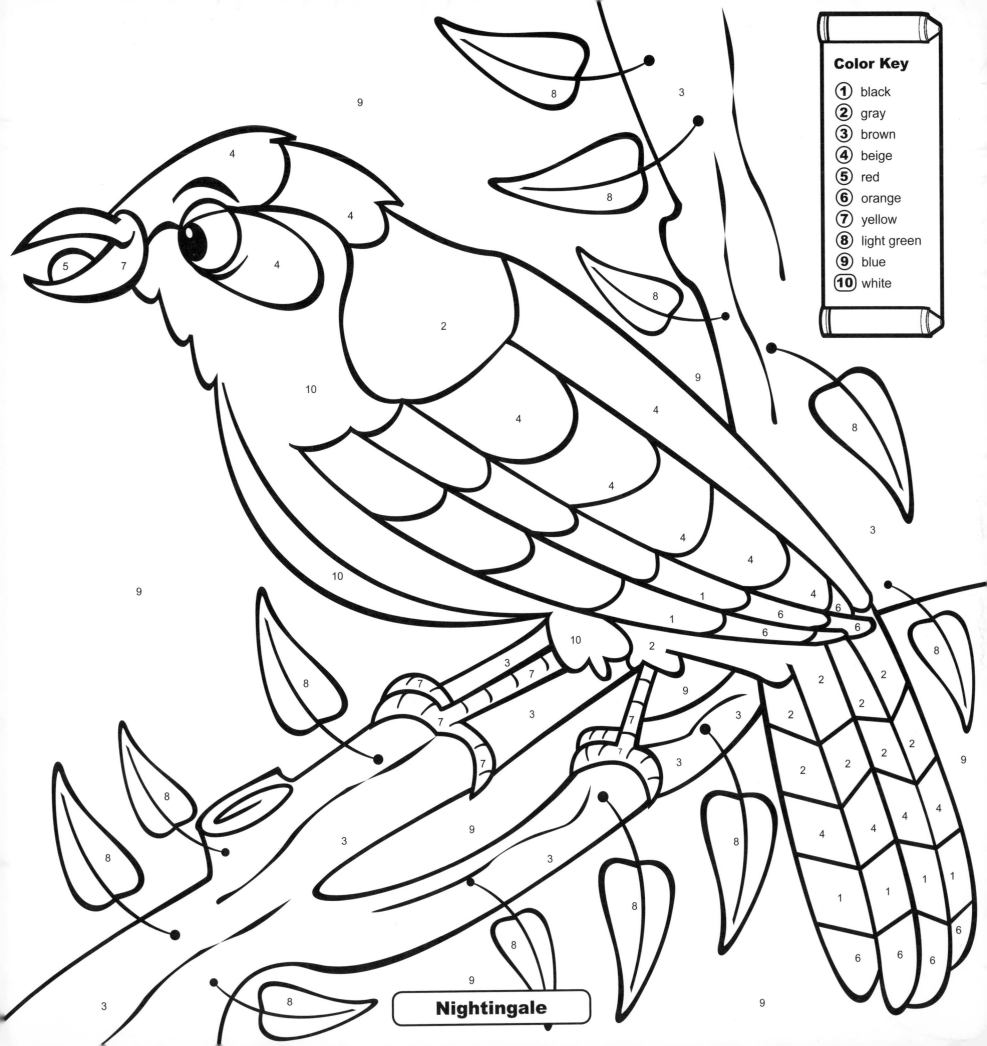

Nightingale

Color Key

1. black
2. gray
3. brown
4. beige
5. magenta
6. pink
7. red
8. orange
9. yellow
10. light blue

Mole

Color Key
1 black
2 gray
3 brown
4 beige
5 red
6 yellow
7 light green
8 blue-green
9 blue
10 white

Badger

Color Key

1. black
2. brown
3. beige
4. red
5. orange
6. yellow
7. light green
8. dark green
9. light blue
10. white

Crane

Color Key
1. black
2. gray
3. brown
4. beige
5. pink
6. red
7. yellow
8. light green
9. light blue
10. white

Reindeer

Color Key
1. black
2. brown
3. beige
4. magenta
5. pink
6. yellow
7. light green
8. green
9. dark green
10. light blue

Norwegian Lemmings

Color Key
1. black
2. gray
3. beige
4. pink
5. red
6. yellow
7. light yellow
8. dark green
9. blue-green
10. white

Bats

Color Key
1. black
2. brown
3. beige
4. magenta
5. pink
6. light green
7. dark green
8. blue
9. light blue
10. white

Dormouse

Color Key

① black
② gray
③ brown
④ beige
⑤ magenta
⑥ pink
⑦ light yellow
⑧ green
⑨ blue-green
⑩ white

Great Grey Owl

Color Key

1 black
2 gray
3 brown
4 beige
5 red
6 orange
7 yellow
8 green
9 blue
10 light blue

Wild Boar

Color Key

1 black
2 gray
3 brown
4 pink
5 red
6 orange
7 light green
8 green
9 blue
10 white

Foxes